BIRD'S BAD DAY

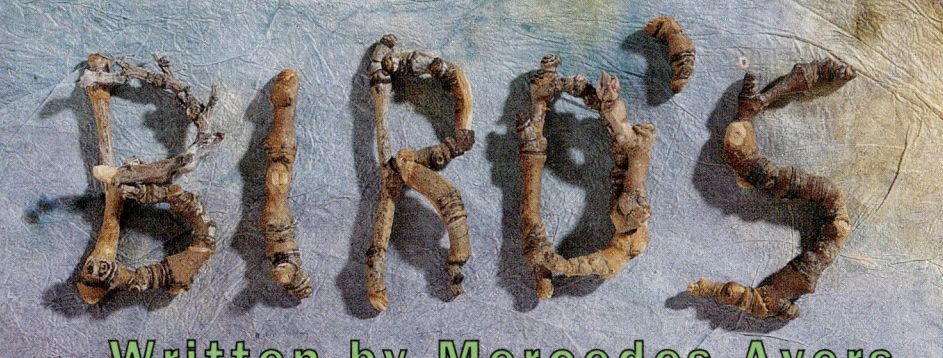

Written by Mercedes Ayers

Illustrated by Leo Yerxa

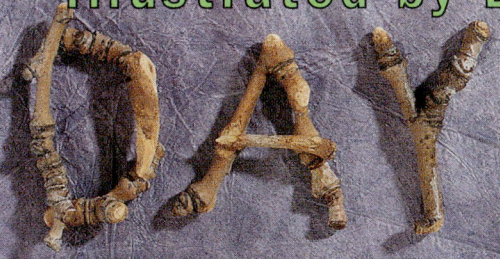

HARCOURT BRACE & COMPANY
Orlando Atlanta Austin Boston San Francisco Chicago Dallas New York
Toronto London

"Here is my lunch," said Bird.

Crack—snapped the branch.

"Here is my nest," said Bird.

Crack—snapped the branch.

"Here is my friend," said Bird.

Crack—snapped the branch.

"What a bad day," said Bird.